# GCSE AQA English
## Producing Non-Fiction Texts and Creative Writing
### The Workbook

This book is for anyone doing **GCSE AQA English**
or **English Language** at higher level.

It contains lots of **tricky questions** designed to hone your **writing skills**
— because that's the only way you'll get any **better**.

It's also got some daft bits in to try and make the whole
experience at least vaguely entertaining for you.

## What CGP is all about

Our sole aim here at CGP is to produce the highest quality
books — carefully written, immaculately presented and
dangerously close to being funny.

Then we work our socks off to get them out to you
— at the cheapest possible prices.

# CONTENTS

## Section Six — The Exam

## Section Seven — Creative Writing

## Section Eight — The Controlled Assessment — English Language

## Section Nine — The Controlled Assessment — English

Published by Coordination Group Publications Ltd.

Editors:
Polly Cotterill
Edmund Robinson
Caley Simpson

Produced with:
Peter Thomas
Alison Smith
Nicola Woodfin

Contributors:
Holly Bennett
Samantha Bensted

With thanks to Luke von Kotze, Carl Dowling and Emma Willshaw for the proofreading.

ISBN: 978 1 84146 943 0

Groovy website: www.cgpbooks.co.uk

Printed by Elanders Hindson Ltd, Newcastle upon Tyne.
Jolly bits of clipart from CorelDRAW®

Based on the classic CGP style created by Richard Parsons.

# How to Use this Book

There's just <u>one exam</u> for GCSE English Language and GCSE English.  It's for <u>Unit 1: Understanding and Producing Non-Fiction texts</u>.  The exam's split into <u>two bits</u> — Section A (<u>reading</u>) and Section B (<u>writing</u>).  This book covers the <u>writing</u> part of the exam.  It'll also help you with the <u>Unit 3 controlled assessment</u>, where you have to do some <u>creative writing</u>.

## The Exam Paper is Broken Down like this

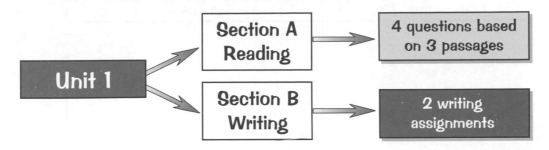

You have <u>2 hours</u> for this exam.

## In the Exam You Do Both Questions in Section B

And that's the part of the brain responsible for Unit 1, Section B...

1)  In Section B there are <u>two writing questions</u>, question 5 and question 6. You have to answer <u>both</u>.

2)  There are <u>16 marks</u> available for question 5 and <u>24 marks</u> for question 6.

3)  You should spend about <u>25 minutes</u> on question 5 and <u>35 minutes</u> on question 6.

4)  In this workbook, there are loads of <u>different questions</u> that cover the <u>different types of writing</u> you might have to do in your exam.

5)  There's a <u>mix</u> of questions — some that only need a <u>short answer</u> and questions that you need to write a <u>little essay</u> for (good practice for your exam).

6)  There are <u>sample exam questions</u> from Section B to give you an idea of what to expect.

## Unit 3 is Different for English Language and English

1)  The <u>Unit 3 controlled assessment</u> is a bit <u>different</u> depending on which GCSE you're doing.

2)  <u>Everyone</u> has to write <u>two pieces</u> of <u>creative writing</u>, chosen from a <u>bank</u> of <u>six tasks</u>.

3)  You have to make sure that the tasks you choose are from <u>different topics</u> — e.g. you can't do two 'Moving Images' tasks.

4)  There's loads more information in the back of this book.  <u>Section 7</u> has some handy <u>practice questions</u> for <u>everyone</u>, <u>section 8</u> has <u>sample tasks</u> and <u>answers</u> for people doing <u>English Language</u>, and <u>section 9</u> is for people doing <u>English</u>.

# Purpose and Audience

Q1 Put each of the writing tools in the box below into the appropriate column of the table, depending on whether they are more suited to descriptive or persuasive writing.

> flattery     details about sounds, sights & smells     details about textures & tastes
>
> facts and statistics     similes & metaphors     rhetorical questions     emotive language

| Descriptive | Persuasive |
|---|---|
|  |  |

Q2 Write down a plan of 5 bullet points, showing how you would structure a speech arguing in favour of school uniform.

1) ...............................................................................................................................

2) ...............................................................................................................................

3) ...............................................................................................................................

4) ...............................................................................................................................

5) ...............................................................................................................................

Q3 Read the following extracts and write down whether their purpose is to inform, explain, describe, argue, persuade or advise.

Geoff's test drive was going well.

a)
> The new Fold Mungeo has all the luxuries that you'd expect from an executive car, yet with a surprisingly affordable price tag. Go down to your local dealer today and ask for a 24 hour test drive.

..............................

b)
> One of the first things you should look for is whether the property has smoke alarms or not. If it doesn't, don't rent it — you want a landlord who cares about the tenants' safety.

..............................

## If the audience falls asleep you're in trouble...

You've got to remember the purpose and audience of your essay. And you've got to keep them in mind all the time that you're writing, or you'll wander off the point. Try to keep focused...

# Purpose and Audience

**Q1** Write down a few sentences that you might use as an introduction to a talk on healthy eating for the following audiences:

a) primary school children

How often do you eat fruit?

...................................................................................................

...................................................................

b) elderly people

...................................................................................................

...................................................................................................

...................................................................

*"Oily fish should eat at least 3 portions of people a week..."*

c) parents

...................................................................................................

...................................................................................................

...................................................................................................

**Q2** Write down a good opening sentence for an answer to each of the questions below. Make sure it's suitable for the audience and purpose of the question.

a) Write the text for a radio programme **informing** listeners about a hobby or interest and **explaining** why more people should take up your hobby.

Do you like football?

...................................................................................................

b) Write an article for a magazine aimed at teenagers in which you **argue** that schools should teach students more practical skills like driving, how to manage money or DIY.

...................................................................................................

c) Write a letter to your head teacher **persuading** him/her to let you take time off school to participate in a national competition on the TV.

...................................................................................................

**Q3** **Describe** a cinema when it's full and when it's empty.

MINI-ESSAY QUESTION

*You'll need some lined paper to write on for the mini-essay questions,.*

# Letters, Adverts, Leaflets and Articles

**Q1** How would you start letters to the following people? The first one has been done for you.

a) Your headmistress

**Dear Mrs Coombes**

..............................................................................................................

b) Your best friend

..............................................................................................................

c) Your local fire safety officer (you don't know their name)

..............................................................................................................

**Q2** Read the following bits of advice for your writing exam and decide if they're true (T) or false (F).

a) You'll get more marks if you draw pictures to illustrate leaflets. (T / F)

b) It's good to use headings, subheadings and bullet points in adverts and leaflets. (T / F)

c) You should write in paragraphs and include plenty of detail in letters. (T / F)

d) You have to put your address at the top to get full marks in a letter-writing question. (T / F)

**Q3** For each of the writing tasks below, write down 3 suitable headings.

a) A leaflet to **inform** new Year 7 students about what to expect from their first year at school.

..............................................................................................................

..............................................................................................................

..............................................................................................................

b) An advert to **persuade** students to subscribe to an online revision site.

.................................................................................................

Welcome to Thrashworts School. Now get out of my sight and don't come back until Year 11.

.................................................................................................

.................................................................................................

**Q4** Write the text for an advertisement which aims to persuade young people to buy a new healthy soft drink.    *MINI-ESSAY QUESTION*

**Q5** Write a leaflet advising teenagers at your school how to deal with bullying.    *MINI-ESSAY QUESTION*

*Section One — Purpose, Audience and Form*

# Other Types of Text

Q1    Read the following bits of advice for your writing exam and decide if they're true (T) or false (F).

a)    If you're asked to write a script for a radio show, you need to write it out like a playscript.  (T / F)

b)    Structure isn't very important when you're writing a script or a speech.  (T / F)

c)    You should try and make your speech or script sound like spoken language.  (T / F)

d)    If you're writing a radio script it's a good idea to talk directly to your audience.  (T / F)

Q2    Read the following extracts from a speech persuading local residents to do more recycling. Write down why you think each extract is effective.  The first one has been done for you.

a)    "I know sometimes it seems like too much effort to sort out your plastic and cardboard rather than just throwing it in the bin."

**Talks directly to the audience — uses 'I' and 'your'.**

**Anticipates audience's response.**

b)    "The landfill sites are full to bursting, heaving with decomposing food and unwanted packaging."

..................................................................................................................................

..................................................................................................................................

c)    "In just two years, all the landfill sites in the county will be full —  then what will we do?"

..................................................................................................................................

..................................................................................................................................

d)    "A recent survey estimated that 70% of landfill rubbish could have been recycled. That means we're not making enough effort to recycle."

....................................................................................................

....................................................................................................

Anya never enjoyed
putting out the rubbish..

Q3    Write a talk to give to your class informing them about a place that you've visited and explaining why you would recommend it to them.

MINI-ESSAY
QUESTION

# At least they don't ask you to write song lyrics...

Or maybe that'd be a lot more fun — writing a song to sing to your local council persuading them of the need for more facilities for young people in your area.  Go on.  I dare you.

# <u>Exam Technique</u>

**Q1** Write down **3** key things that you could underline when you're looking at a writing exam question.

1) .................................. 2) .................................. 3) ..................................

**Q2** For each of the following exam questions, write down the key points that you'd make in your essay as well as any ideas you have about the style or form that you would use in your answer.

a) Write an advice leaflet telling young children about basic road safety.

...............................................................................................

...............................................................................................

...............................................................................................

b) Write a speech arguing against the statement that 'young people today have an easy life'.

...............................................................................................

...............................................................................................

...............................................................................................

c) Describe a room you know well.

...............................................................................................

...............................................................................................

...............................................................................................

**Q3** Draw a spider diagram plan for an answer to the following exam question:
'Write a letter to your head teacher arguing that students should have more choice in what they study.'

**Q4** Now write a full essay for the following exam question: Write a speech, to be given at your local youth club, arguing against the statement that 'young people today have an easy life'.

MINI-ESSAY QUESTION

*Section One — Purpose, Audience and Form*

# <u>Exam Technique</u>

Q1   Rewrite the following rather dull paragraph to make it more interesting.

> Last week was our school play.  I was supposed to be one of the main characters.  Unfortunately, right before the dress rehearsal, I lost my voice.  Everyone was very shocked.  I took lots of cough medicine but it didn't help.  Someone else had to speak my lines.  I just stood there looking like an idiot.  Luckily my voice came back on the night of the performance and I was really good.

.............................................................................................................................................................................

.............................................................................................................................................................................

.............................................................................................................................................................................

.............................................................................................................................................................................

.............................................................................................................................................................................

.............................................................................................................................................................................

Q2   a)   Write an introductory paragraph for an essay describing a school at night.

.............................................................................................................................................................................

.............................................................................................................................................................................

.............................................................................................................................................................................

.............................................................................................................................................................................

.............................................................................................................................................................................

b)   Write the concluding paragraph of an essay explaining which famous person you'd like to be and why.

.............................................................................................................................................................................

.............................................................................................................................................................................

.............................................................................................................................................................................

.............................................................................................................................................................................

.............................................................................................................................................................................

Q3   Now write a full essay for question 2(b) above — explain which famous person you'd like to be and why.

MINI-ESSAY QUESTION

# Spelling and Punctuation

Q1  Put commas and full stops where they're needed into the sentences below.

a)  I jumped out of the taxi narrowly missing a very large puddle by the kerb

b)  Keeley said she wanted an MP3 player a pair of shoes and some more make-up

c)  As the boat glided past its bright paint glinting in the sun I was able to see the captain saluting me his gold braid fluttering in the breeze

Q2  Copy out each of the sentences below, putting apostrophes in the correct places.

a)  Its easy to learn to ski if youre not afraid of falling.

It's not the falling that bothers me, mate — it's the hard landing...

........................................................................

b)  We looked everywhere but we did'nt find Ruperts ball or the ponies's carrots.

........................................................................

Q3  Copy the sentences below and replace full stops and commas with semicolons, question marks or exclamation marks where appropriate.

a)  I didn't want to go.  The leaden sky seemed too threatening to set out.

........................................................................

b)  Have you ever wondered what it would be like to travel in time.  It'd be fantastic.

........................................................................

c)  You can come to my party as long as you bring an expensive present, stay until the end, clear up any spillages, hand round the peanuts and don't drink any alcohol.

........................................................................

........................................................................

Q4  Tick the boxes next to the words that are spelt correctly and correct those spelled wrongly.

arguement ☐      unnatural ☐      concsious ☐

neccessarily ☐      disappear ☐      immediately ☐      consience ☐

favorite ☐      embarassed ☐      decieved ☐      occasional ☐

Q5  Circle the correct word to fill in the gaps in these sentences.

a)  This afternoon (we're/were) going to Scarborough (were/where) you can buy fish and chips.

b)  I'd like to borrow (you're/your) bike, if (you're/your) not using it today.

c)  (We're/where) going nearer the stage, because I can't (here/hear) the band from (here/hear).

*Section One — Purpose, Audience and Form*

# Writing to Inform and Explain

Q1    Use the words in the box below to fill in the gaps in this passage about writing to inform.

| detail sophisticated bored something opinion inform language |

Writing to ....*inform*.... is simply when you write to tell the reader about ....*something*.... or someone. You'll mostly be writing facts, but it's OK to include your own ....*opinion*...., personal stories and some interesting ....*detail*.... to keep the reader from getting too ....*bored*..... The most important part of writing to inform is using varied, interesting ....*language*...., which will make your writing look ....*sophisticated*.....

Robostudent is rubbish at writing to inform. He can blame his programming, but you can't.

Q2    Underline the types of text below which are examples of writing to inform.

A letter to your pen friend telling her about your town

Script for a radio comedy show

Advert for a new type of washing powder

Web page about different types of tractors

Letter to the council asking for more money to be spent on recycling

Problem page in a magazine

Q3    Circle the types of writing below that are examples of **explanations**.

Questionnaire asking how much sport people do

Instructions for an MP3 player

Gallery guidebook telling you how Picasso did his paintings

Letter to the Police apologising for stealing traffic cones

Set of road directions from Bangor to Richmond

Email asking permission to borrow someone's golf clubs

Q4    Do you think the style of these explanations is appropriate for the audience? Circle your answer.

a)    A talk for primary school children explaining how they can stay safe on the roads.

"Statistics show that most pedestrian fatalities take place at night and when facing away from oncoming traffic." **YES / NO**

b)    A letter to a bank manager explaining why you're a good candidate for a loan.

"As you can see, I have an impeccable payment record with my credit card." **YES / NO**

c)    A letter of complaint to your local Italian restaurant, explaining why you're unhappy.

"When I raised my concern with the waiter, he was very rude. I shall not be visiting your establishment again." **YES / NO**

# Audience and Form

**Q1**    Read the piece of informative text below and then answer the questions that follow.

> GCSE Grades To Hit New High
> When this year's estimated GCSE results are published by the Department for Education this week, it is predicted that a new record will be set. The number of pupils achieving at least five GCSEs at grades A*-C is expected to rise from 53 per cent to 57 per cent. This would mean the biggest increase in over a decade.

a)    Describe the most likely **audience** of this piece of text. Give a reason for your answer.

*Adults/Parents .*
*- Statistics being used / very detailed.*

b)    Rewrite the text using language that would be suitable for a magazine aimed at GCSE students.

............................................................................................................................

............................................................................................................................

............................................................................................................................

**Q2**    Underline the correct word(s) from each pair to complete the sentences below.

> Objective writing is written from a **personal / balanced** viewpoint. When you're writing objectively you should try to include lots of **facts / opinions** so that you sound more **emotional / convincing** . Subjective writing on the other hand is much more **factual / one-sided** and contains more **controversial points / statistics** .

**Q3**    Circle whether each of these explanations is **objective** or **subjective**.

a)    I felt completely lost when I arrived at the ferry port because it's totally different from how the guidebook describes it.    **Objective / Subjective**

b)    Most clouds are composed of water droplets but ones at higher altitudes contain ice crystals, which is why they have a different appearance.    **Objective / Subjective**

c)    I wouldn't bother going to see that film if I were you. The actors' delivery is terrible and the ending is completely ridiculous — she'd never fall in love with him just because he wasn't afraid of her dog.    **Objective / Subjective**

# Structure and Techniques

Q1    Imagine you're writing an information leaflet for tourists about a local wild animal park.

a)    Write the introduction section of the leaflet. Don't worry about including made-up facts.

*Are you an animal lover? Or do you just enjoy strolling around an animal park? Well, either way, your at the right place, ensuring that you have a fabulous day.*

b)    Give at least **three** points that you could include in your leaflet.
Remember to think carefully about the structure and how you'll organise your points.

*• A map / directions for the tourists who don't know their way around.*

*• Include sections on each bit of the wild animal park.*

*• Make sure the tourists are clear on where to go if they need a drink or have come across some kind of problem.*

Q2    Cross out the incorrect word in each pair to complete the following sentences.

a)    Explanations should be easy to follow — one way to do this is to include ~~quotes~~ / subheadings to break up the text.

b)    When you're explaining something, it's generally best to write as clearly / ~~elaborately~~ as possible and to include as many details / ~~paragraphs~~ as you can.

c)    Including lots of examples / ~~opinions~~ is a good way to make your writing sound authoritative.

Q3    Match the following features of a text to the reasons you might use them in informative writing.

a)    Subheadings                    **To make your writing less boring for the reader**

b)    Technical terms                 **To engage the reader by provoking a reaction**

c)    Emotive language              **To direct the reader through your points**

d)    Interesting vocabulary       **To make yourself sound knowledgeable on a subject**

---

# But I've never been to a wild animal park...

Well that's fine, the good thing about English exams is that you can make things up. Just write about things like lions and elephants and monkeys breaking bits off your car, and a café. Job done.

# Writing Your Own

Q1    Look at the extract from a piece of informative writing below.  Then answer the questions that follow.

> Queen Elizabeth's Grammar School
> What's on offer for your child?
> At QEGS, we're proud to offer not only the expected subjects and activities, but also a huge range of qualifications in diverse subjects and an unusually large variety of after-school activities.
> Your child will have the opportunity to undertake the following:
> • GCSE and A-Level Japanese (including a Japanese exchange programme)
> • GCSE and A-Level Cake Studies

a)    Explain the purpose of the subheading in the text above.

*It summerises whats going to be in the paragraph.*

b)    Write another subheading that could be used for a section in the text about the school's facilities.

*School's facilities.*

c)    Write another section of the leaflet that could come after this subheading:
<u>Sport?  We've got it covered</u>

*The sports we do are very exciting and we can assure you that your child will find P.E inter and action packed...*

Q2    Below are some facts about children in Victorian times.  Read the facts and then write a first person **explanation** of what it was like to be a child in Victorian times, for a GCSE History textbook.  Include as much detail as you can in the space provided.

**children were often employed from the age of seven for very low wages**

**children often worked in mines, mills or as chimney sweeps**

*It was very terrifying and intimedatio*

Q3    Write a letter to a friend informing them of a memorable event from your childhood.  [MINI-ESSAY QUESTION]

Q4    Write a speech, to be given to teachers and professionals at a careers evening, about what you'd like your life to be like when you're twenty-five years old.  [MINI-ESSAY QUESTION]

*Section Two — Writing to Inform and Explain*

# Writing Your Own

Q1    Write the introduction to an account of how you woke up and got ready this morning.

.................................................................................................................................

.................................................................................................................................

.................................................................................................................................

Q2    Below is a fairly boring piece of writing. Rewrite it adding as much interesting detail and sophisticated vocabulary as you can fit into the space provided.

> When I was seven I lived in Bridlington. It was nice but it was cold sometimes. I played on the beach all the time and went to the amusement arcade. Then we moved to Scunthorpe and I was sad.

.................................................................................................................................

.................................................................................................................................

.................................................................................................................................

.................................................................................................................................

.................................................................................................................................

.................................................................................................................................

Q3    Write a point you'd put in an answer to each of the following questions. Make sure you include an example to back up each point.

a)    Name a famous person that you'd like to meet and **explain** why.

.................................................................................................................................

.................................................................................................................................

b)    Describe a time when you felt nervous and **explain** why.

.................................................................................................................................

.................................................................................................................................

Q4    Write a newspaper article **explaining** what you think could be done to improve GCSE results.   MINI-ESSAY QUESTION

## Explain why writing to explain often explains...

I would like to explain to you why I'm afraid of CAPITAL LETTERS. I believe that there are a number of reasons for my crippling phobia, but it all started when I was 7, and in Mr Mead's English class...

# Writing to Describe

**Q1**  Look at the following exam question, then write down two different **viewpoints** you could use to write your answer.

a)  Describe a wood at night.

......................................................................................................................................

......................................................................................................................................

b)  Describe an ideal holiday destination.

...............................................................................................................

"360-degree sea views..."

...............................................................................................................

**Q2**  Write one descriptive sentence about a busy leisure centre based on each of the following senses:

a)  sight

......................................................................................................................................

b)  sound

......................................................................................................................................

c)  touch

......................................................................................................................................

d)  smell and / or taste

......................................................................................................................................

**Q3**  You've been asked to describe a beach.  Imagine you're videoing the scene and write a few sentences to describe what you're filming at each of the following points:

a)  Aerial view of the beach:

......................................................................................................................................

......................................................................................................................................

b)  The area around the beach, e.g. the promenade, cliffs or sand dunes:

......................................................................................................................................

......................................................................................................................................

c)  Close-up on the sand, rocks or sea:

......................................................................................................................................

......................................................................................................................................

# <u>Imagery</u>

Q1     Read the sentences below then write down if they're examples of **similes** or **metaphors**.

   a)   As I approached the front door, I felt my stomach contract as if it was being squeezed in a vice.

   ..................................................

   b)   A thick duvet of snow covered the ground and kept our hiding place snug.

   ..................................................

   c)   The fluorescent lighting of the chip shop reflected off the metallic lines of the counter and the uncompromising plastic benches.  It looked like some kind of weird, greasy hospital.

   ..................................................

   d)   The fox froze for a moment, one paw raised, before slipping across the road and through the railings by the railway line; a red ghost captured in my car headlights.

   ..................................................

Q2     Write a sentence for each of the following descriptions:

   a)   Use personification to describe a car.

   ........................................................................................

   b)   Use a metaphor to describe an urban landscape.

   ........................................................................................

   c)   Use a simile to describe the feeling of embarrassment.

   ........................................................................................

Q3     Use imagery to describe the following things (you can choose which type of imagery to use):

   a)   Feeling excited.

   ........................................................................................

   ........................................................................................

   b)   A cave.

   ........................................................................................

   ........................................................................................

   c)   A fire.

   ........................................................................................

   ........................................................................................

# Techniques

Q1  Rewrite each pair of short sentences below into one longer, complex sentence. The first one has been done for you.

a)  He raised his arm for a cab.  A passing bus splashed water on his trousers.

**As he raised his arm for a cab, a passing bus splashed water on his trousers.**

.................................................................................................................................

b)  I ran headlong down the path.  I didn't know whether Henry was following me.

.................................................................................................................................

c)  The beach seemed deserted.  One solitary little boy was trawling aimlessly in the rock pools.

.................................................................................................................................

Q2  Write down some sentences you might use to describe the scenes below:
Make sure you use a variety of sentence types and descriptive writing techniques in your answers.

a)  A theme park...

in summer:  ......................................................................................................

.................................................................................................................................

.................................................................................................................................

in winter:  ............................................................................

.......................................................................................

........................................................................................

b)  Your school...

on your first day there:  ...............................................................

.................................................................................................................................

now:  ...................................................................................................

.................................................................................................................................

c)  A supermarket...

during the day:  ..............................................................................

.................................................................................................................................

at night:  .........................................................................................

.................................................................................................................................

# Writing Your Own

Q1  Write an opening sentence for an answer to each of the exam questions below.
Try to make your sentence really effective so your reader wants to read on.

a)  **Describe** someone you'd like to have lunch with.

.......................................................................................................................................

.......................................................................................................................................

b)  **Describe** your favourite place.

.......................................................................................................................................

.......................................................................................................................................

c)  **Describe** what you think life will be like for people 300 years from now.

.......................................................................................................................................

.......................................................................................................................................

*Who are these "people" of whom you speak?*

Q2  Now try writing a couple of sentences to finish an answer to the following exam questions.
Try to make your ending really effective.

a)  **Describe** your least favourite place.

.......................................................................................................................................

.......................................................................................................................................

b)  **Describe** a person who is very important to you.

.......................................................................................................................................

.......................................................................................................................................

c)  **Describe** a local town or city.

.......................................................................................................................................

.......................................................................................................................................

Q3  **Describe** your favourite place and **explain** why you like it so much.    MINI-ESSAY QUESTION

Q4  **Describe** one of your friends.    MINI-ESSAY QUESTION

# Writing to Argue and Persuade

Q1    Look at the exam question below and then fill in the table to give the purpose, form and audience of this question.

| Purpose | |
|---------|---|
| Form | |
| Audience | |

Write a letter to your local council, arguing that there should be more facilities for teenagers in your local area.

Q2    For each of the arguments below, circle the option that the writer is arguing **for**.

a)    How can they be allowed to get away with this?  There's plenty of money available to feed our children a decent, healthy meal every lunchtime, yet they're being fed reconstituted mystery meat with chips.  I'm appalled.  It's no wonder childhood obesity and diabetes are on the rise.

healthier school meals
OR
school meals as they are

b)    Why do people need to travel so far away?  Why can't they just holiday at some of the beautiful British seaside resorts?  The world is warming up and the climate is changing thanks to our insistence on flying everywhere in those polluting, gas-emitting giants of the sky.  It's got to stop.

more air travel
OR
less air travel

Q3    Read the extract below from a piece of persuasive writing and then answer the questions that follow.

Ladies and gentlemen, thank you for attending our demonstration of the amazing industrial cleaning powers of the "Wizzitron 590".  Today, you'll witness state-of-the-art solar-powered cleaning which will change the way you think about your business' cleaning needs forever.
        The "Wizzitron 590" will not only enable you to be at the forefront of the environmental revolution, but it will also save your business thousands.  At our introductory price of only £999.99, surely this is an offer you can't refuse?

a)    What is the writer trying to persuade the audience to do?

.......................................................................................................................................................

b)    Do you think this extract is from a speech, a letter or an article?  Explain your answer.

.......................................................................................................................................................

.......................................................................................................................................................

c)    Who is the audience?  Give an example from the text to show how you know.

.......................................................................................................................................................

.......................................................................................................................................................

# Structure and Techniques

Q1 Imagine you're writing a letter to your local council persuading them to clear up the rubbish dumped in your local area. Write extracts from the letter using the techniques listed below.

a) Rhetorical question

..........................................................................................................................

..........................................................................................................................

b) Exaggeration

..........................................................................................................................

..........................................................................................................................

c) Emotive language

..........................................................................................................................

..........................................................................................................................

Q2 Imagine you're writing a letter to your head teacher arguing that year 11 should be provided with a common room. Write short extracts from this letter using the techniques suggested below.

a) facts and statistics

..........................................................................................................................

..........................................................................................................................

b) personal anecdotes

..........................................................................................................................

..........................................................................................................................

Q3 For each of the exam questions below, write a few lines that use the past, present and future tenses.

a) Write a speech for your school assembly in which you argue that sport at school should be optional.

..........................................................................................................................

..........................................................................................................................

b) Write an article for a newspaper in which you argue that hunting and fishing should be banned.

..........................................................................................................................

..........................................................................................................................

Q4 Write a full letter for Q1 above, making sure you include the parts you've already written. Remember to use the right tone for the audience and to start and end the letter appropriately.

MINI-ESSAY QUESTION

# Structure and Techniques

Q1    Read the following extracts from a speech arguing that sport should be given more priority in schools. Write down which writing techniques are used and why you think they're effective. The first one has been done for you.

a)    "Of course the UK's relatively poor performance in sporting events has nothing to do with a lack of support for sport in schools — it's far more likely that toxins in our drinking water make us poor batsmen and give us mediocre racquet skills."

**The extract uses satire. This is effective because it looks at first as though it's supporting**

**the counter-argument, but then you find that it's actually ridiculing the counter-argument.**

b)    "The answer is simple: it takes practice, practice and yet more practice, with some hard work thrown in for good measure."

.........................................................................................................................

.........................................................................................................................

c)    "A report from the Sports' Association found that many children are simply not given the opportunity to try a wide range of track and field sports at school."

.........................................................................................................................

.........................................................................................................................

Q2    Read the extracts below from pieces of persuasive writing. Then state what technique has been used to persuade the reader, and explain why you think this is effective. The first one has been done for you.

a)    "This is clearly the highest quality, most cleverly designed MP3 player on the market."

**Uses assertion — presenting opinions as if they're facts.**

**This is effective because it makes the writer's opinion sound like it's true.**

b)    "We understand that an intelligent, responsible person such as yourself will be horrified that this sort of behaviour is tolerated. Your support can help us put a stop to it."

.........................................................................................................................

.........................................................................................................................

c)    "Hundreds of innocent children are affected by this painful, often crippling disease. Paul, a courageous, fun-loving boy, never gave up hope and is now thriving thanks to kind donations."

.........................................................................................................................

.........................................................................................................................

Q3    Write an article for a magazine aimed at teenage boys in which you argue in favour of a healthier lifestyle.

MINI-ESSAY
QUESTION

# Writing Your Own

**Q1**  Look at the words and phrases below.  Copy them into the correct columns of the table to show whether they are used to present an argument, develop an argument, or present a counter-argument.

It is clear that

On the other hand

Also

Furthermore

In addition

Although some people argue that

In my opinion

| Presenting an argument | Developing an argument | Presenting a counter-argument |
|---|---|---|
|  |  |  |

**Q2**  Draw lines to match the sections of an exam answer with where they should be found.

a)  Strong concluding section which reinforces the main points.

b)  Section which builds on the points made in the previous paragraph, offering solutions where possible.

c)  Short section which briefly introduces the main problem.

d)  Section which offers alternative solutions to those already offered.

first paragraph

second paragraph

third paragraph

final paragraph

**Q3**  Read the exam question and then answer the questions below.

> Write the text for a speech to be given in your school assembly, in which you attempt to persuade fellow students to boycott the school canteen until they bring back unhealthy snacks.

a)  What is the form, purpose and audience in this question?

Form: ............................  Purpose: ............................  Audience: ............................

b)  Write a rhetorical question which you could use in this speech.

..................................................................................................................

c)  Make up some believable facts or statistics which you could include.

..................................................................................................................

..................................................................................................................

d)  Write a sentence for your speech which contains some emotive language.

..................................................................................................................

..................................................................................................................

# _Writing Your Own_

Q1    Imagine you've been asked to write a speech for your school assembly arguing that anyone found guilty of bullying another student should be instantly expelled.

     a)   Write a short introduction for your speech.

        ......................................................................................................................................

        ......................................................................................................................................

     b)   Write a conclusion for your speech.

        ......................................................................................................................................

        ......................................................................................................................................

        ......................................................................................................................................

Q2    Now write a full answer for Q1, using what you've already written above.    MINI-ESSAY QUESTION

Q3    Read the exam question below and then answer the questions that follow.

> Write a letter to your head teacher persuading him or her to allow students to borrow laptops from the school for their homework projects.

     a)   Write an introductory paragraph to the letter.

        ......................................................................................................................................

        ......................................................................................................................................

        ......................................................................................................................................

     b)   List **two** persuasive points that you could make in your answer.

        ......................................................................................................................................

        ......................................................................................................................................

     c)   Write a final, concluding paragraph to the letter.

        ......................................................................................................................................

        ......................................................................................................................................

        ......................................................................................................................................

# Writing to Advise

**Q1**    Underline the types of text below which are examples of written **advice**.

Autobiography of a reality TV star          Web page on how to conserve energy

Magazine article on interesting             Letter to the council asking for
ways to save money                          more facilities for teenagers

Holiday advert for the Maldives             Problem page in a magazine

Script for a radio comedy show              Leaflet on how to stop smoking

**Q2**    Write down whether the following statements about written advice are **true** or **false**.

a)  Written advice tells people what action to take about something.              ....................

b)  You should always write advice in a very formal, official writing style.      ....................

c)  It's best to write advice in an indirect way, rather than addressing the reader directly.   ....................

d)  Written advice often gives the reader a variety of options to choose from.    ....................

e)  When writing advice, you should let the reader know you understand their feelings.   ....................

**Q3**    For each of the exam questions below, write whether your writing style should be **formal** or **informal**.

a)  Write an article for a magazine for teenagers, advising
them on the best ways to make friends at a new school.      ...........................

b)  Write a letter to your local MP, advising him or her on
how best to find out the opinions of young people.          ...........................

c)  Write a script for a local radio show in which you advise
listeners on easy ways to save money at Christmas.          ...........................

Formal or informal was never
an issue for Julie and Mike.

**Q4**    For each of the following pieces of advice, write out either a **formal** or
**informal** version of the same advice.  The first one has been done for you.

a)  **Formal:** You should resist the urge to react to any provocation.

   **Informal:** If anyone bothers you, just ignore them. ...........................................................................

b)  **Informal:** I think you should sell your car.

   **Formal:** ...........................................................................................................

c)  **Formal:** My colleague believes that you should resign from your position.

   **Informal:** ...........................................................................................................

d)  **Informal:** Don't marry the first bloke you set eyes on.

   **Formal:** ...........................................................................................................

# *Writing Style*

Q1    The extract below is from a leaflet **advising** teenagers on coping
with revision.  Read it and then answer the questions that follow.

> School exams are highly important, as they are the gateway to further academic achievement
> and career advancement.  It is imperative that everyone who sits an exam is thoroughly
> prepared, otherwise failure and ultimate downfall will result.  The key to successful
> preparation is adopting an unyielding approach combined with an imperturbable attitude.

a)    Do you think the tone of this extract is appropriate for the audience?  Explain your answer.

.......................................................................................................................

.......................................................................................................................

b)    Does the extract address the reader directly or not?  Do you think this is appropriate?

.......................................................................................................................

.......................................................................................................................

c)    Write a **more appropriate** piece of revision advice for teenagers.  Your answer doesn't have to be
based on the extract but you can use it as a starting point if you like.

.......................................................................................................................

.......................................................................................................................

.......................................................................................................................

.......................................................................................................................

Q2    Suggest a possible heading for each of the texts (to **advise**) listed below.

a)    Leaflet for tourists        ...........................................................................................

b)    Book on pet care        ...........................................................................................

c)    Careers advice pamphlet        ................................................................................

Q3    Below is a piece of **advice** that needs a
better layout.  Write a title and subheading
for it and separate out the advice with
bullet points.

...........................................................................................

...........................................................................................

> Eat at least five portions of fruit and
> veg a day.  Eat wholegrain bread and
> cereal.  Drink eight glasses of water
> a day.  Avoid fatty, salty and sugary
> snacks.

...........................................................................................

...........................................................................................

...........................................................................................

...........................................................................................

# Structure and Techniques

Q1  For each of the following exam questions, give one piece of **advice**, stating **how**, **when**, **where** and **why** the reader should take your advice.  The first one has been done for you.

a)  Write the text for a leaflet **advising** children to wear cycle helmets.

**Every time you ride your bike, whether you're on the road or just in the park, remember to wear your cycle helmet.  It'll stop you being seriously hurt if you fall and hit your head.**

b)  Write the text for a speech **advising** teenagers how they can do their bit to help the environment.

..........................................................................................................................................

..........................................................................................................................................

..........................................................................................................................................

c)  Write an article for a newspaper **advising** people how to cope with using euros when they're abroad.

..........................................................................................................................................

..........................................................................................................................................

..........................................................................................................................................

Q2  Choose words from the box to fill in the gaps in the passage below about writing to **advise**.

> formally   directly   tone   informal   understand   advise

When you're writing to ............................... , it's very important to use a reassuring ............................... . Tell the reader that you ............................... how they're feeling.  It helps to address the reader ............................... by using words like 'you'.  The tone of writing to advise needs to be matched to the audience.  When the advice is about something serious it's usually best to write ............................... , but for more light-hearted topics it's better to be ............................... .

Q3  Write a full answer to question 1(b) — a speech **advising** teenagers how they can do their bit to help the environment.

MINI-ESSAY QUESTION

---

# Never listen to advice...

Actually when people start advising you to do something in an "I know it all" tone of voice it's really tempting to ignore them and do just the opposite.  Which is exactly how I fell down that well...

# *Writing Your Own*

Q1    Read the introduction below from a piece of **advice** for young people about starting a new school. Then answer the questions that follow.

> <u>Starting at a new school — scary but exciting</u>
>
> So you're about to start at secondary school? You're probably feeling rather nervous. Well, don't worry; we've all been there at some point and we've lived to tell the tale. It can be weird being the youngest in the school again, but after the first week or so you'll be making lots of new friends and doing lots of exciting new activities. Just to reduce the stress a bit, here are some handy hints on how to cope at first.

a)    How does the tone of this piece of writing help it achieve its purpose? Explain your answer.

.......................................................................................................................................

.......................................................................................................................................

b)    What sort of language has been used in the piece? Is it appropriate for the intended audience?

.......................................................................................................................................

.......................................................................................................................................

c)    Draw a spider diagram to plan a leaflet for young people starting a new school.

"It may seem strange at first, but don't forget to file your exercise books in the bin after every lesson. It's a school rule."

d)    Write out one point that you'd include in the main part of this piece of writing. Remember to state how, when, where and why.

.......................................................................................................................................

.......................................................................................................................................

e)    Write a short concluding paragraph for this piece of writing.

.......................................................................................................................................

.......................................................................................................................................

.......................................................................................................................................

Q2    Now write the full text for an **advice** leaflet for young people starting a new school. Use the introduction and your conclusion from Q1 if you like.    MINI-ESSAY QUESTION

---

*Section Five — Writing to Advise*

# Exam Questions — Inform/Describe Question

If you've ever sat in an exam thinking how much easier it would be to <u>mark essays</u> than to write them, this is the section for you. Yep, that's right, you get to read a load of <u>exam answers</u> and decide which <u>grade</u> you think they deserve. It'll help you understand what <u>examiners</u> are <u>looking for</u> — which will help you write <u>better answers</u>. Here's how you do it:

1) <u>Read</u> the sample exam question below and make sure you understand it.
   You <u>don't</u> have to answer the question.

2) Have a look at the <u>mark scheme</u> explaining <u>how to mark</u> the answers.
   On the next few pages there are some <u>example answers</u> for you to mark yourself.

When you first read an exam question, make sure you underline the <u>purpose</u>, the <u>audience</u> and the <u>form</u>. You need to keep these things in mind whether you're <u>writing</u> an answer or <u>marking</u> one.

---

**Section B: Writing**

Answer **both** questions in this section.

You are <u>advised to spend about one hour</u> on this section.
You are advised to spend about 25 minutes on question 5.
You are advised to spend about 35 minutes on question 6.

---

5   Write an <u>informative leaflet</u> for <u>children</u> visiting a wildlife park <u>describing an animal</u> of your choice.

*(16 marks)*

       *Form*       *Audience*       *Purpose*

---

Next, have a look at the <u>mark scheme</u>. Read along each row to get an idea of what an answer needs to include to get a particular <u>grade</u>.

| Grade | What you've written | How you've written | Spelling, punctuation and sentence structures |
|---|---|---|---|
| C | Quite detailed points with appropriate tone, interesting vocabulary and some use of different writing techniques. | Written with clear structure, in paragraphs, and with a clear identification of purpose and audience. Clear development of ideas. | Some fairly complex sentences, generally accurate spelling, good simple punctuation. |
| B | Good range of vocabulary and writing techniques to engage the reader. Viewpoint clearly sustained throughout the text. | Well structured, with form, content and style mostly matched to audience and purpose. Paragraphs used well, ideas well thought out and presented. | Varied sentence choices, accurate spelling of most words, accurate and useful punctuation. |
| A | Ambitious and imaginative vocabulary. Writing techniques used to engage the reader. | Fluently linked sentences and paragraphs consistently matching form, content and style to audience and purpose. Answers show logic and creativity. | Clear and controlled variation of sentence structures, accurate spelling, good range of accurate punctuation. |
| A* | Convincing, confident, compelling points combining a range of details, using writing techniques successfully. Complex, possibly abstract ideas presented effectively. | Fluently linked sentences and paragraphs consistently matching form, content and style to audience and purpose. Answers show logic and creativity. Sophisticated structure. | Wide range of sentence structures successfully used, sophisticated and accurate spelling and punctuation. |

# Sample Exam Answers — Inform/Describe

Deciding what grade to give can be a pretty tricky business. First off, make sure you've <u>read through</u> the answer a couple of times so you know what it's all about. When you think you've got a good grasp of what the writer is saying, there are <u>three main things</u> you need to think about.

<u>What's written</u>
- Does the writer stick to the topic?
- Is there enough information?
- Does the writer make points clearly and imaginatively?
- Is the vocabulary interesting?

<u>How it's written</u>
- How well organised is the text?
- Does the order of sentences and paragraphs make the text easy to understand?
- Has the writer used the right sort of language for the audience and purpose?

<u>Spelling and Punctuation</u>
- Are the spelling and punctuation accurate and sophisticated?
- Does the writer build sentences in several different ways — simple, complex and compound?

Have a look at this worked example answer to the question on page 27.

**Answer 1**

> <u>The World's Tallest Animal</u>
> Giraffes are the tallest animal on the planet — their legs alone are about the same height as a room and their necks are longer than the tallest man you can imagine. When you put all their body parts together, they're so tall they could look over the top of a double decker bus. Our tallest giraffe is called Jeremy, and he's a whopping 5.3 metres tall! Giraffes are friendly animals, and tend to live in herds.

This part of the answer would get grade **B** because the writer has thought about the audience, and used language that children could understand. They could also relate to the comparisons used to describe how tall the giraffes are. However, the vocabulary isn't very interesting (they repeat the word 'tall' a lot) and the heading could be more exciting.

Now it's your turn to have a go at marking one:

**Answer 2**

> <u>Parrot Patter Pulls in the Punters!</u>
> Cheeky, chirpy and cheerful... parrots are a popular bird here at Pets Corner. With their emerald green, ruby red and golden yellow feathers, they are also one of the most brightly-coloured, creating a dazzling display as they fly over visitors' heads. But it's not just his colourful feathers that make a particular parrot called Percy so popular — he's clever enough to talk! Percy can imitate people's voices, so you might find him repeating what you say.

This part of the answer would get grade ☐ because ....................................

..................................................................................................................
..................................................................................................................
..................................................................................................................
..................................................................................................................

# Sample Exam Answers — Inform/Describe

Here are some more lovely examples for you to mark. Make sure you keep referring to the <u>mark scheme</u> on page 27. The answer probably won't fit the descriptions perfectly, so your job is to work out which description is the <u>best fit</u> for the answer.

Here's a quick reminder of what you need to do:

1) Read through the <u>mark scheme</u> and the <u>question</u> on <u>page 27</u>.
2) Read carefully through the <u>answer 3 extract</u> a couple of times.
3) Ask yourself the <u>questions</u> on <u>page 28</u>.
4) Compare the <u>extract</u> to the <u>mark scheme</u> and decide which <u>grade description</u> matches it best.
5) Then do the same thing for the <u>answer 4 extract</u>.

**Answer 3**

> Elephants
> The most striking thing about an elephant is probably it's size. It's as big as an army tank! The second most striking thing or rather things are its massive ears, which it uses to fan itself when it's hot. But the most unique thing about an elephant is its trunk, which is actually a really long nose, but can do a lot more things than most noses. For example, as well as using it for breathing and smelling things, an elephant uses its trunk to trumpet, to drink water, and even to pick things up.

*Don't forget these are just extracts from answers — your exam answers will have to be longer.*

This part of the answer would get grade ☐ because ...................................................

................................................................................................................................

................................................................................................................................

................................................................................................................................

................................................................................................................................

**Answer 4**

> The snout of a pig, the ears of a donkey, the body of a badger, the tail of a kangaroo, and a tongue like a long, sticky, wriggly worm... No, it's not the list of ingredients for a witch's potion. No, it's not the unfolded result of one of those draw-the-head-fold-it-over-pass-it-on games. And no special effects or artificial additives were used in the making of this peculiar looking creature. Believe it or not, it's a real live animal... It's the aardvark! Aardvarks are also known as anteaters because (you guessed it) they like to eat ants — their long tongues are perfect for licking them up.

This part of the answer would get grade ☐ because ...................................................

................................................................................................................................

................................................................................................................................

................................................................................................................................

................................................................................................................................

# Exam Questions — Argue/Persuade Question

Assessing <u>other people's work</u> is a brilliant way of <u>improving your own writing</u>, so here come some more <u>sample answers</u> for you to mark. Don't say I never give you anything.

1) <u>Read</u> the sample exam question below and make sure you understand it.
   You <u>don't</u> have to answer the question.

2) Have a look at the <u>mark scheme</u> explaining <u>how to mark</u> the answers.
   On the next few pages there are some <u>example answers</u> for you to mark yourself.

Remember to keep in mind the <u>purpose</u>, the <u>audience</u> and the <u>form</u>.

---

**Section B: Writing**

Answer **both** questions in this section.

You are advised to spend about one hour on this section.
You are advised to spend about 25 minutes on question 5.
You are advised to spend about 35 minutes on question 6.

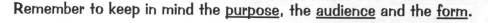

*Form* → → ← *Audience*

6    Write a <u>column</u> for a <u>newspaper</u> arguing either for or against a year of compulsory National Service for all school leavers, where they have to help the environment in some way. ← *Purpose*

*(24 marks)*

---

Now have a good look at the <u>mark scheme</u>. Each row shows you the kind of level that an answer should be written at to be awarded a particular <u>grade</u>.

| Grade | What you've written | How you've written | Spelling, punctuation and sentence structures |
|-------|--------------------|--------------------|----------------------------------------------|
| C | Quite detailed points with appropriate tone, interesting vocabulary and some use of different writing techniques. | Written with clear structure, in paragraphs, and with a clear identification of purpose and audience. Clear development of ideas | Some fairly complex sentences, generally accurate spelling, good simple punctuation. |
| B | Good range of vocabulary and writing techniques to engage the reader. Viewpoint clearly sustained throughout the text. | Well structured, with form, content and style mostly matched to audience and purpose. Paragraphs used well, ideas well thought out and presented | Varied sentence choices, accurate spelling of most words, accurate and useful punctuation. |
| A | Ambitious and imaginative vocabulary. Writing techniques used to engage the reader with a clear awareness of opposing viewpoints. | Fluently linked sentences and paragraphs consistently matching form, content and style to audience and purpose. Answers show logic, persuasive thoughts and creativity. | Clear and controlled variation of sentence structures, accurate spelling, good range of accurate punctuation. |
| A* | Convincing, confident, compelling points combining a range of details, using writing techniques successfully. Complex, possibly abstract ideas presented effectively. | Sophisticated structure that matches form, content and style to audience and purpose (to argue, persuade or advise). Answers show logic, persuasive thoughts and creativity. | Wide range of sentence structures successfully used, sophisticated and accurate spelling and punctuation. Opposing viewpoints used for effect. |

# Sample Exam Answers — Argue/Persuade

Here's a reminder of the kind of things you need to be looking out for when you're <u>marking</u>:

### What's written
- Does the writer stick to the topic?
- Is there enough information?
- Does the writer make points clearly and imaginatively?
- Is the vocabulary interesting?

### How it's written
- How well organised is the text?
- Does the order of sentences and paragraphs make the text easy to understand?
- Has the writer used the right sort of language for the audience and purpose?

### Spelling and Punctuation
- Are the spelling and punctuation accurate?
- Does the writer build sentences in several different ways — simple, complex and compound?

Now see how you get on with marking these <u>sample answers</u> for the <u>argue/persuade</u> question.

**Answer 1**

<u>Surprise Landslide for The Completely Bonkers Party?</u>
"When you're eighteen..." How many times have I heard that? When you're eighteen you can make your own choices — you can choose to get married, to drink yourself into oblivion or to vote for The Completely Bonkers Party "just for a laugh". And now — a mere five hundred and twenty-seven days from my eighteenth birthday — you want to take away my right to make my own decisions about my own life. Personally I have little desire to get married or drink myself into oblivion, but I may well decide to vote for The Completely Bonkers Party if that's the only way of ensuring that this out-dated, ageist and hypocritical legislation isn't passed...

This part of the answer would get grade [ ] because ............................................

................................................................................................................................

................................................................................................................................

................................................................................................................................

................................................................................................................................

**Answer 2**

<u>A Brighter Future for Everyone</u>
Where I live, there aren't many opportunities to do something interesting, and the boredom really gets to you sometimes — I'm sure that's why my older brother's been in a few scrapes. Of course, some of the richer kids go on gap years to exciting places to help out in local communities and feel good about themselves, but for the poorer kids, whose parents can't afford to help them out with the money, it's just not an option. Well, we'd all like to feel good about ourselves and get some respect from other people, and I think helping the environment would be a great way to do it...

This part of the answer would get grade [ ] because ............................................

................................................................................................................................

................................................................................................................................

................................................................................................................................

................................................................................................................................

# Sample Exam Answers — Argue/Persuade

Just to make sure you've really got the hang of this marking malarkey, here are a couple more extracts for you to have a go at. Just in case you've forgotten, here's what you have to do:

1) Read through the mark scheme and the question on page 30.
2) Read carefully through the answer 3 extract a couple of times.
3) Ask yourself the questions on page 31.
4) Compare the extract to the mark scheme and decide which grade description matches it best.
5) Then do the same thing for the answer 4 extract.

**Answer 3**

Your Planet Needs You

The Earth is in trouble. The amounts of greenhouse gases like carbon dioxide and methane in the atmosphere have rocketed over the last century, species are becoming extinct as we destroy their habitats and everywhere you look there's waste and pollution. Although my generation isn't directly responsible for causing these problems, our lives and those of our children depend on us cleaning up the mess that has been left. It's our responsibility to make sure the world is habitable for future generations.

By introducing compulsory National Service for school leavers, not only would we make sure of a cleaner, healthier future for our planet, we'd also make sure each generation understood the importance of looking after the environment, and knew how to do so. Since we are the next generation of industrialists, scientists and politicians, surely this is the best way of making sure that the people in charge know what they must do to save the planet...

This part of the answer would get grade ☐ because ..............................

..................................................................................................

..................................................................................................

..................................................................................................

..................................................................................................

**Answer 4**

School Leavers – The Ultimate Cheap Renewable Resource?

Many years ago, children were sent down mines, up chimneys, and out to pick pockets. Now the so-called responsible adults of this world want to commission the youth of today to clean up their toxic mess. So what's changed?

I think it's a disgrace that in an allegedly democratic country this preposterous idea has attracted any support at all. Of course the youth of today are concerned about the environment, of course we want to do our bit to help (it's our future after all), but on a voluntary basis. If we are deprived of our right to do the right thing freely and of our own choice, then what meaning does the action have? Aren't we simply creating a culture where each generation knows that it can pass responsibility for its failings on to the next?...

This part of the answer would get grade ☐ because ..............................

..................................................................................................

..................................................................................................

..................................................................................................

..................................................................................................

# Writing About Moving Images

**Q1**   Write a review of a film you have been to see recently.
The review is for your school magazine.

..................................................................................................................................

..................................................................................................................................

..................................................................................................................................

..................................................................................................................................

..................................................................................................................................

**Q2**   Write the beginning of a voice-over for a documentary about your town.

..................................................................................................................................

..................................................................................................................................

..................................................................................................................................

..................................................................................................................................

..................................................................................................................................

**Q3**   Read the short-story extract below and explain what features make it suitable for making into a film.

> The early morning sun sent rays of honey-kissed light over the park. Some tendrils of mist still lingered as Elena made her way to the river, making her shiver and wrap her arms around herself. The mist clung to her long auburn hair and left its droplets on her summery cardigan. It was only just after dawn, and the park was deserted. She couldn't help but make comparisons between a similar spring morning only a year ago. A morning that she would never forget...

**Q4**   Write the voice-over for an advert for a new type of biscuit.   *MINI CONTROLLED ASSESSMENT TASK*

**Q5**   Write a short story that could be the basis for a crime drama. Include lots of visual details to give the director ideas about how you imagine the characters and settings.   *MINI CONTROLLED ASSESSMENT TASK*

# Writing on a Particular Theme

Q1    You have been asked to write a piece of creative writing based on the theme 'Colour'. In the box below, draw a spider diagram showing your ideas.

Happy Birthday, I'm your Spider-o-gram...

Q2    Write the introduction to a story beginning with the line: "I never want to see you again," he said.

..................................................................................................................................

..................................................................................................................................

..................................................................................................................................

..................................................................................................................................

..................................................................................................................................

..................................................................................................................................

Q3    Write a column for a magazine with the heading: "If only I'd..."    MINI CONTROLLED ASSESSMENT TASK

Q4    Choose one of your ideas from Q1 and use it to write a creative piece on the theme 'Colour'.    MINI CONTROLLED ASSESSMENT TASK

Q5    Using your introduction for Q2, write the rest of the short story.    MINI CONTROLLED ASSESSMENT TASK

# Changing the Genre of a Text

Q1   Write the introduction to a newspaper article based on the events in a poem you have studied. Don't forget to write an appropriate headline too.

..............................................................................................................................................

..............................................................................................................................................

..............................................................................................................................................

..............................................................................................................................................

..............................................................................................................................................

..............................................................................................................................................

..............................................................................................................................................

Q2   The following extract shows how you might adapt William Golding's *Lord of the Flies* into an article. Use the example to write the beginning of a short story, based on the events in the article.

## FEARS GROW FOR MISSING SCHOOLBOYS

A group of schoolboys is missing and feared dead after the plane carrying them was shot down somewhere over the Pacific. The wreckage of the plane was discovered 1,000 miles off the coast of Chile, with the body of the pilot, named today as Captain Frederick Armitage, still inside. The plane had been attacked by enemy forces. However, none of the passengers have been found, suggesting that the boys on board may have escaped alive. Rescue teams are searching the nearby area for signs of life.

The plane was carrying over 50 British schoolboys being evacuated from the war, including the choir of Christchurch School, London. Mrs Merridew, mother of missing choirboy Jack, spoke exclusively to our reporter this morning: "I'm so worried about my boy Jack, I just want him home again. But he can take care of himself, he's the head boy and chapter chorister. He can sing C sharp."

Q3   Choose an event from a text you have studied and use it to write an article for a women's magazine.   MINI CONTROLLED ASSESSMENT TASK

Q4   Write a short story based on a play you have studied. You can use lines from the play as dialogue if you want.   MINI CONTROLLED ASSESSMENT TASK

# Writing From Your Point of View

**Q1**  Write the introduction to a 'real-life' magazine article based on a scary experience.

........................................................................................................

........................................................................................................

........................................................................................................

........................................................................................................

........................................................................................................

........................................................................................................

........................................................................................................

**Q2**  Make a plan for a speech to a Year 7 class about your first year at secondary school.

**Q3**  Read the extract below and pick out the features that show this is a personal account.

> I can't remember the last time I felt so relaxed. I'd slept well, had a lovely breakfast and was now sitting in the garden in the morning sun reading a book. It was idyllic. I could smell the orange blossom and hear the birds singing to each other. Cup of tea in hand, could this be any more perfect?

**Q4**  Write a short story with the title "My favourite holiday".    *MINI CONTROLLED ASSESSMENT TASK*

**Q5**  Write a newspaper article about your favourite band.    *MINI CONTROLLED ASSESSMENT TASK*

# Mark Scheme

The Unit 3 Controlled Assessment is a bit different depending on whether you're doing the English Language GCSE, or English. If you're doing English Language, this section is for you. If you're taking English you can skip right on ahead to section nine.

## Look at Content, Structure and Accuracy

Remember, these are the three things the markers are always looking for when they're marking.

- **WHAT'S WRITTEN** — Does it stick to the topic? Are points made clearly and imaginatively? Is the language suitable for the audience and purpose?
- **HOW IT'S WRITTEN** — Do the sentences and paragraphs follow on from each other smoothly? Do they hang together to make a well-structured piece of writing?
- **SPELLING AND PUNCTUATION** — Are the spelling and punctuation accurate? Are the sentences formed in several different ways — simple, complex and compound?

## Here's a Mark Scheme telling you How to get each Grade

This mark scheme shows what the markers look for when deciding which grade to give your piece of creative genius. They'll work out which of the statements in this table best fits your work.

| Grade | What you've written | How you've written | Spelling, punctuation and sentence structures |
|---|---|---|---|
| C | Detailed points with appropriate tone, interesting vocabulary and some use of different writing techniques. | Written with clear structure, in paragraphs, and with a clear identification of purpose and audience. | Some fairly complex sentences, generally accurate spelling, good simple punctuation. |
| B | Good range of vocabulary and writing techniques to engage the reader. Sustained writing. | Well structured, with form, content and style mostly matched to audience and purpose. Paragraphs well organised and used to develop ideas. | Some varied and sometimes bold sentence choices, accurate spelling of most irregular and complex words, accurate and useful punctuation. |
| A | Ambitious and imaginative vocabulary. Writing techniques used creatively to engage the reader. | Fluently linked sentences and paragraphs consistently matching form, content and style to audience and purpose. Answers show logic, persuasive thoughts and creativity. | Clear and controlled variation of sentence structures, accurate spelling, good range of accurate punctuation. |
| A* | Convincing, confident and compelling writing combining a range of details, using writing techniques coherently. Complex, possibly abstract ideas presented effectively. | Sophisticated structure that matches form, content and style to audience and purpose. Answers show logic, persuasive thoughts and creativity. Structure used effectively to enhance main points. | Wide range of sentence structures successfully used for effect, sophisticated vocabulary with accurate spelling and correct punctuation. |

# Moving Images

Here are some <u>sample answers</u> for you to <u>mark</u> and give the grade you think they deserve.

Here's how to start:

1) Follow the advice and mark scheme on page 37.
2) Read the task carefully.
3) Look at answer 1 and read the comments that follow (we've done this first one for you).
4) Mark the extract in answer 2 (below) using the mark scheme. It's not the full answer but should give you the gist.
5) Give it the grade you think it's worth and explain why.

> Write a review of a film you have seen recently. The review will be part of a television programme.

**Answer 1**

<u>Coming up... Bright Star shines (5 stars)</u>
 Bringing poetry to the big screen's never easy, but Jane Campion's film triumphs on most levels, showing that Keats's works were inspired by tragic love. From the touching of hands against walls to the poetry voice-overs, there wasn't a dry eye left in the house.
 The love that grows between the poet John Keats (played expertly by Ben Whishaw) and English rose Fanny Brawne is played out through his moving letters and poetry. Think that's not going to work for cinema? Think again. When Keats writes that he wishes they were as free as butterflies, lonely Fanny hatches a bedroom of butterflies which creates a spectacle of blue fluttering insects. The music is crafted to create feeling and understanding about her painful emotions and you can feel their frustration.

This part of the answer would get grade **A\*** because **it's clearly written as a review, and is appropriate for a TV programme. The words and tone used are right for the audience, and it uses interesting vocabulary. It comments on key scenes, images, the soundtrack and acting. The spelling and punctuation are good and the answer is organised into paragraphs. The title works well for a TV trailer and the star rating shows the student has understood the purpose of the task.**

Now here's one for you to mark:

**Answer 2**

<u>Not such a Bright Star</u>
 John Keats was an incredibly talented poet, but in this film I was disappointed that you don't get to hear the true range of his amazing poetry. Though you get the feeling of tragedy in how hard love is when their apart you don't feel you have got to the heart of it or understood why his poems have lived on, or why they touched Fanny Brawne so much that she lived and breathed them.
 Fanny spends a lot of the time feeling sorry for herself, interrupting him when he's busy working. I felt that the sad beauty of Ode to a Nightingale was lacking as the actor's voice was too dull for a man who's feeling desperate.

This part of the answer would get grade ☐ because ........................................

..............................................................................................................

..............................................................................................................

..............................................................................................................

..............................................................................................................

# Commissions

It's your lucky day — here's another sample task for you to mark without having to answer the question yourself.

Here's a quick reminder of what you need to do:

1) Read the task carefully.

2) Remember to follow the mark scheme on page 37.

3) Read answer 1 and award it the grade you think it's worth, saying why you gave it that grade.

4) Do it again for the answer 2 extract.

*Learning why you award the marks will help you get maximum points for your answers.*

> A national magazine has chosen you as their new columnist and has asked you to write an article on the theme of 'Parents'.

---

**Answer 1**

Parents and grandparents

When my grandparents died my mum was heartbroken. To her parents were what made feel safe and secure, and when she lost her father to old age it was like she'd lost part of her. I don't think that anyone wants to think about it really, but thankfully I don't have to because mine are still really young (as my dad says, there's plenty of life in the old man yet).

That's not to say I don't get annoyed like any other teenager does when they ask me to pick up my shoes or put the lid on the toothpaste. And there's times when I want to scream when they don't let me stay out late (even though I'm always sensible)! They say its for my own good but sometimes I wonder. I often dream of living on my own but if I was honest, I do need them because parents do have their positives (though I hate to admit it).

This part of the answer would get grade ☐ because ..................................................

..............................................................................................................

..............................................................................................................

..............................................................................................................

..............................................................................................................

---

**Answer 2**

Can't live with them...

The other day I heard a phrase we all know. Two men were swapping stories on the bus, moaning about their wives and how they're always nagging them ("She never lets up!" the skinny one complained) and the other sighed, took his cap off and said "Can't live with them, can't live without them." That's how I feel about parents.

Most teenagers battle against their parents on a daily basis. Parents become irritated by the small things, like leaving tea stained cups strewn across the floor, being sullen and moody (as if!), and before you know it, you've got World War III on your hands. The trouble is that more than anything teenagers need their parents rather more than they'd like to admit.

This part of the answer would get grade ☐ because ..................................................

..............................................................................................................

..............................................................................................................

..............................................................................................................

..............................................................................................................

*Section Eight — The Controlled Assessment — English Language*

# Re-creations

Nearly there — there's just time for another task and another chance to fine-tune your marking skills.

Remember, you'll need to:

1) Read the mark scheme one more time (page 37).
2) Give the answers the grades you think they deserve.
3) Explain why you think they should get that grade.

> Write a non-fiction or journalistic piece based on the content, themes and ideas in a poem from the AQA Anthology.

These answers are based on 'The Wild Swans at Coole' by W. B. Yeats (from the Literary Heritage section of the anthology).

**Answer 1**

Local beauty spot under threat
   Residents of Coole are up in arms. Their beautiful lake and woodland, which puts on a stunning display of colour in autumn could be bulldozed, as plans are rumoured to be in place to build houses on that very spot.
Special site
   Nature lovers and the Environment Agency argue that the woodland (pictured) is home to nearly 60 thriving swans, many with young. The many visitors who spend time there, writing or walking, will have nowhere else to be amongst nature. As Councillor Scott said, "There's nothing like the spectacle of these swans at twilight when they soar above you. If they fly away they need to have somewhere safe to return to. Where will they go if it's destroyed?"

This part of the answer would get grade ☐ because ....................................................
..............................................................................................................................
..............................................................................................................................
..............................................................................................................................
..............................................................................................................................

**Answer 2**

Out and about in Coole
   Looking for somewhere to stretch your legs this weekend? Look no further than Coole in Ireland, where the lake and woodland paths there can offer you bracing fresh air.
   At Coole you can walk around the edges and see the beautiful butterflies and bullrushes. Best of all, you'll see a whole group of swans swimming in the water, guiding their cygnets along.
   You can then take a break and find a spot to have a picnic. Autumn is a perfect time to see it, so why not also visit the harvest festival in Coole, not far from the lake?

This part of the answer would get grade ☐ because ....................................................
..............................................................................................................................
..............................................................................................................................
..............................................................................................................................
..............................................................................................................................

# Mark Scheme

This section has sample tasks and answers for anyone doing the Unit 3 Creative Writing Controlled Assessment for the English GCSE. First up, here's a mark scheme to have a look at.

## Look at Content, Structure and Accuracy

Remember, these are the three things the markers are always looking for when they're marking.

- **WHAT'S WRITTEN** — Does it stick to the topic? Are points made clearly and imaginatively? Is the language suitable for the audience and purpose?
- **HOW IT'S WRITTEN** — Do the sentences and paragraphs follow on from each other smoothly? Do they hang together to make a well-structured piece of writing?
- **SPELLING AND PUNCTUATION** — Are the spelling and punctuation accurate? Are the sentences formed in several different ways — simple, complex and compound?

## Here's a Mark Scheme telling you How to get each Grade

This mark scheme shows what the markers look for when deciding which grade to give your piece of creative genius. They'll work out which of the statements in this table best fits your work.

| Grade | What you've written | How you've written | Spelling, punctuation and sentence structures |
|---|---|---|---|
| C | Detailed points with appropriate tone, interesting vocabulary and some use of different writing techniques. | Written with clear structure, in paragraphs, and with a clear identification of purpose and audience. | Some fairly complex sentences, generally accurate spelling, good simple punctuation. |
| B | Good range of vocabulary and writing techniques to engage the reader. Sustained writing. | Well structured, with form, content and style mostly matched to audience and purpose. Paragraphs well organised and used to develop ideas. | Some varied and sometimes bold sentence choices, accurate spelling of most irregular and complex words, accurate and useful punctuation. |
| A | Ambitious and imaginative vocabulary. Writing techniques used creatively to engage the reader. | Fluently linked sentences and paragraphs consistently matching form, content and style to audience and purpose. Answers show logic, persuasive thoughts and creativity. | Clear and controlled variation of sentence structures, accurate spelling, good range of accurate punctuation. |
| A* | Convincing, confident and compelling writing combining a range of details, using writing techniques coherently. Complex, possibly abstract ideas presented effectively. | Sophisticated structure that matches form, content and style to audience and purpose. Answers show logic, persuasive thoughts and creativity. Structure used effectively to enhance main points. | Wide range of sentence structures successfully used for effect, sophisticated vocabulary with accurate spelling and correct punctuation. |

# Is it just me — or is the word 'scheme' a bit sinister?

Looking at these mark schemes can make a huge difference to your work. Knowing the sorts of things that the markers are looking for, makes it a lot easier to get what they want into your work.

# Moving Images

Here are some <u>sample answers</u> for you to mark and give the <u>grade</u> you think they <u>deserve</u>.

Here's how to start:

1) Follow the advice and mark scheme on page 41 (it's based on the one that markers use).
2) Read the task carefully.
3) Look at answer 1 and read the comments that follow (this first one's been marked for you).
4) Mark answer 2 using the mark scheme — it's not the full answer but it should give you the gist.
5) Then give it the grade you think it's worth, and say why you awarded it that grade.

> Write a story for an adventure film designed for the big screen. Include visual detail for the director and try to create atmosphere for cinema-goers.

**Answer 1**

Forever Running (Cert 18)

The immense plain dwarfed him as he cowered in the burning sand, exhausted and drained, with no breath left in his wheezing lungs.

With aching limbs and bruised feet he slumped to the ground, as parched as the desert he'd become lost in. It was the hottest part of the day and he'd started to hallucinate, imagining visions of quenching water. He was feeling alone and half-crazed under the orange sun, his cotton shirt drenched and dark with sweat, his face burned and sore.

Suddenly, growing louder and louder, and with increasing speed, he heard the drumming sound he feared more than anything. Squinting into the blinding light he could make out two, then three, then four terrifying figures in battle dress. Each shape grew larger and more threatening with each second. With fear and panic he realised the dreadful truth: they'd found him.

This part of the answer would get grade **A** because **it creates atmosphere and tension, ideal for a film. It considers what would work well visually (and what sounds could be added), with lots of description, using different senses. It's exciting and the uses interesting vocabulary. The punctuation and spelling are accurate. It's imaginatively written and has an appropriate title. It's organised into paragraphs and uses a variety of sentence structures.**

Now here's one for you to mark:

**Answer 2**

Don't stop running

Lost in the middle of The Dead Sea, she felt more lonely than ever and wondered if she would ever return home to her family, to the place she truly belonged.

The gentle breeze wafted her long brown hair across her eyes and as she scraped it away she realised that a cold tear was falling down her cheek. She'd had to get away from the disaster zone but could see in her mind's eye the children of the flood she'd left behind her, their pitiful figures stamped in her mind. Nothing could be worse than their fate, she thought. Little did she know that an hour later she'd be battling some very deep waters herself.

This part of the answer would get grade ☐ because ............................................

............................................................................................................

............................................................................................................

............................................................................................................

............................................................................................................

# Prompts and Re-creations

It's your lucky day – here's another sample task for you to mark without having to answer the question yourself.

Here's a quick reminder of what you need to do:

1) Read the task carefully.

2) Remember to follow the mark scheme on page 41.

3) Read answer 1 and award it the grade you think it's worth, saying why you gave it that grade.

4) Do it again for the answer 2 extract.

*Learning why you award the marks will help you get maximum points for your answers.*

> Write a creative piece which follows on from the opening line: "The house was being consumed by a host of angry flames and black, billowing smoke".

**Answer 1**

As the flames grew higher, hotter and angrier everyone ran for their lives, coughing and grabbing loved ones and not knowing who or what had started the fire, or why it was this house again.

A flash of blue lights flashed through the darkness and jets of water attacked the fire from all directions. Everyone breathed a sigh of relief because they'd heard that fires remove curses, and for two decades they'd lived under the shadow of this terrible building, shuddering every time they went past it.

This part of the answer would get grade [ ] because ...................................................

..................................................................................................................................

..................................................................................................................................

..................................................................................................................................

..................................................................................................................................

**Answer 2**

Two men grappled with her arms to hold her back, but they were powerless in the face of her determination. Wailing her daughter's name through hot tears, she ran towards the intense, deadly heat, climbing through the smashed bay window, navigating her way through the choking smoke.

The spiral staircase — once something she loved — was now her enemy, as it became a fountain of flames, each step burning as she tried, wheezing and spluttering, to reach the bedroom. She slammed the door to buy herself some time but the heat still chased her. Without a second passing, she went to the oak wardrobe to grab the box, frustrated and flustered (why oh why had she locked it?). The paint on the door was blistering with the heat, but she couldn't move for tears. She wanted to save every memory of her daughter; each lock of hair and precious photograph, since she was snatched from her arms that terrible winter's night.

This part of the answer would get grade [ ] because ...................................................

..................................................................................................................................

..................................................................................................................................

..................................................................................................................................

..................................................................................................................................

# Me, Myself, I.

Nearly there — there's just time for another task and another chance to fine-tune your marking skills.

Remember, you'll need to:

1) Read the mark scheme one more time (page 41).

2) Read the task carefully.

3) Give the answers the grades you think they deserve and explain why they should get that grade.

> Write a piece with the title 'My Most Memorable Summer'.
> Use whatever form you feel could best lead to an effective piece of writing.

---

**Answer 1**

I'd lived in my family home since being carried back from hospital as a tiny, lively, very vocal baby (or so I'm told). For 14 blissful years I became familiar with every crack in the ceiling, every loose floorboard and each intricate flower detail on the lounge curtains. I knew exactly how long it took me to stroll to school (nine minutes, or eight in the rain). But all this was about to come crashing down on me when I heard the news: that summer we'd be moving to Edinburgh.

I couldn't believe my ears. The words, uttered by my world-weary father and said so quickly it was as if they were as unimportant as changing our brand of cereal, rang around my ears. My mind was bombarded with images of life as I knew it (what about Ted, our ragged Yorkshire Terrier and my closest ally? What about netball?). It could hardly bear thinking about, and now I had to go to school and pretend that my world wasn't collapsing before me.

This part of the answer would get grade ☐ because ..................................................

..................................................................................................................

..................................................................................................................

..................................................................................................................

..................................................................................................................

---

**Answer 2**

I'd never been further west than Oxford (about 14 miles as the crow flies). I didn't want to think about five whole weeks away in an alien culture. My mum said it would be "the best experience" and a "once in a lifetime chance", but I just tried to block it all out, and sat at the kitchen table glaring at my breakfast.

I really hoped the summer camp programme wasn't going to give me a place. The thought of a whole month away from everything I knew, my friends, my tarantula, playing cricket... I just couldn't do it. It was just all too much. What relief that I saw sense, because that summer was the most motivating time of my young life.

This part of the answer would get grade ☐ because ..................................................

..................................................................................................................

..................................................................................................................

..................................................................................................................

..................................................................................................................

..................................................................................................................